Hold The Fort, Snoopy!

**Selected cartoons from
DOGS DON'T EAT DESSERT
and YOU'RE ON THE
WRONG FOOT AGAIN,
CHARLIE BROWN**

Charles M. Schulz

CORONET BOOKS
Hodder and Stoughton

PEANUTS comic strips by Charles M. Schulz

Copyright © 1985, 1987 by United Feature Syndicate, Inc

First published in the United States of America in 1988 by Ballantine Books

This book comprises selected cartoons from DOGS DON'T EAT DESSERT and YOU'RE ON THE WRONG FOOT AGAIN, CHARLIE BROWN and is reprinted by arrangement with Pharos Books

Coronet edition 1989

British Library C.I.P.

Schulz, Charles M.
  (Charles Monroe), 1922–
  Hold the fort, Snoopy: selected cartoons from Dogs don't eat dessert and You're on the wrong foot again, Charlie Brown.
  1. American humorous strip cartoons Collections from individual artists
  I. Title
  741.5'973

ISBN 0 340 50642 3

Printed and bound in Great Britain for Hodder and Stoughton Paperbacks, a division of Hodder and Stoughton Ltd., Mill Road, Dunton Green, Sevenoaks, Kent TN13 2YA.
(Editorial Office: 47 Bedford Square, London WC1B 3DP) by
Cox & Wyman Ltd., Reading.

Hold the Fort, SNOOPY!

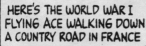

HERE'S THE WORLD WAR I FLYING ACE WALKING DOWN A COUNTRY ROAD IN FRANCE

AH! A BEAUTIFUL FRENCH LASS APPROACHES...

QUICKLY HE CONSULTS HIS PHRASE BOOK

BONJOUR, MONSIEUR..IL FAIT UN TEMPS SUPERBE

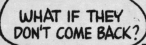

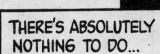

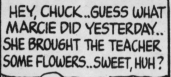

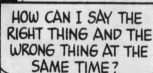

THESE ARE COMMAS AND THESE ARE
POSSESSIVES..COMMAS DO ALL THE
WORK AND POSSESSIVES GET ALL THE
CREDIT..THEY HATE EACH OTHER!

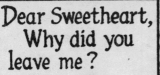

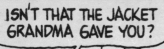

THIS IS A GREAT GOLF HOLE..ONE OF THE BEST IN THE WORLD...

THE FAIRWAY IS LINED WITH BEAUTIFUL OAK AND PINE TREES...

THE WHITE SAND IN THE BUNKERS SPARKLES IN CONTRAST TO THE DEEP SHADES OF THE GREEN...

BEFORE I PLAY A HOLE, I ALWAYS FLATTER IT!

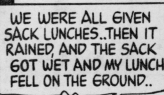

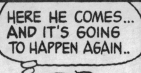

YOU DON'T CARE ANYTHING ABOUT ANYBODY...

YOU NEVER SHOW ANY INTEREST IN WHAT ANYONE ELSE IS DOING..YOU NEVER ASK QUESTIONS...

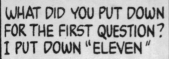

5-22

I WAS PRAYING FOR GREATER PATIENCE AND UNDERSTANDING, BUT I QUIT...

I WAS AFRAID I MIGHT GET IT

5-26

SCHULZ

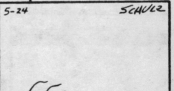

THESE ARE "DELETE" SIGNS

THEY LOOK NICE.. IF I EVER NEED SOMETHING DELETED, I'LL CALL YOU...

I'D LOVE TO DO IT!

5-28

6-2

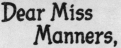

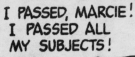

6-23

HERE'S THE FIERCE JUNGLE ANIMAL PERCHED IN A TREE READY TO POUNCE ON A VICTIM WHO PASSES BELOW..

WHAT CAN YOU EXPECT FROM SOMEONE WHO GRADUATED AT THE BOTTOM OF HIS CLASS AT POUNCE SCHOOL?

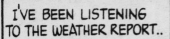

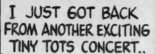

SUPPERTIME!!

PLUNK!

AS THE YEARS GO BY, A GOOD MANAGER GETS TO KNOW HIS PLAYERS..

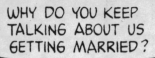

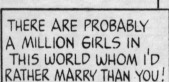

WHERE HAVE YOU BEEN?

WALKING THROUGH THE WOODS NEAR THE GOLF COURSE LOOKING FOR LOST BALLS TO SELL...

DID YOU MAKE ANY MONEY?

7-2

JUST ENOUGH TO PAY FOR THE POISON OAK SHOTS!

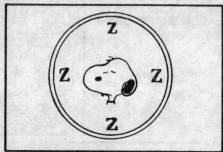

PEANUTS

featuring "Good ol' CharlieBrown"

by SCHULZ

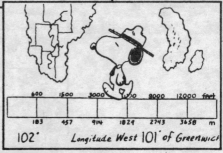

OKAY, TROOPS, TODAY WE'RE GOING TO LEARN ABOUT DIRECTIONS AND MAP READING..

8-4

REMEMBER WHAT I TOLD YOU ABOUT THE MOON? YOU CAN ALWAYS TELL WHICH WAY IS WEST BECAUSE THE MOON IS ALWAYS OVER HOLLYWOOD...

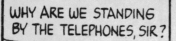

MORE TITLES AVAILABLE FROM
HODDER & STOUGHTON PAPERBACKS

All these books are available at your local bookshop or newsagent, or can be ordered direct from the publisher. Just tick the titles you want and fill in the form below.

Prices and availability subject to change without notice.

Hodder & Stoughton Paperbacks, P.O. Box 11, Falmouth, Cornwall.

Please send cheque or postal order, and allow the following for postage and packing:

U.K. – 55p for one book, plus 22p for the second book, and 14p for each additional book ordered up to a £1.75 maximum.

B.F.P.O. and EIRE – 55p for the first book, plus 22p for the second book, and 14p per copy for the next 7 books, 8p per book thereafter.

OTHER OVERSEAS CUSTOMERS – £1.00 for the first book, plus 25p per copy for each additional book.

Name ....

Address ....

....